(The Id)

The characters in this manga don't age that much, though many years have passed in the story. They're supposed to be immortal, so please pretend to be immortal yourself as you read it!!

Ryu Fujisaki

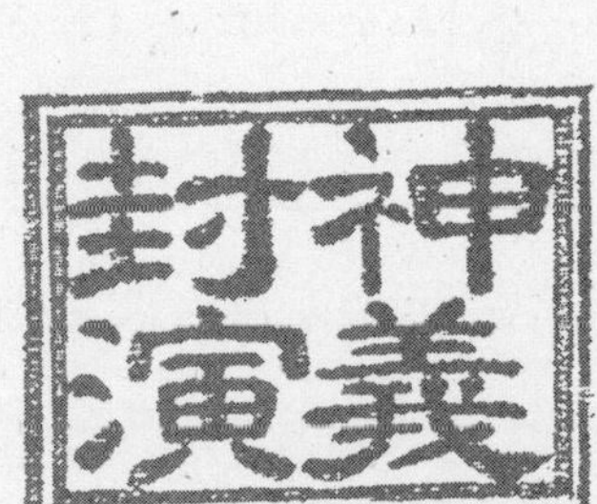

Ryu Fujisaki's *Worlds* came in second place for the prestigious 40th Tezuka Award. His *Psycho +*, *Wāqwāq* and *Hoshin Engi* have all run in *Weekly Shonen Jump* magazine, and *Hoshin Engi* anime is available on DVD in Japan and North America. A lover of science fiction, literature and history, Fujisaki has made *Hoshin Engi* a mix of genres that truly showcases his amazing art and imagination.

HOSHIN ENGI VOL. 8
The SHONEN JUMP Manga Edition

STORY AND ART BY RYU FUJISAKI
Based on the novel *Hoshin Engi*, translated by Tsutomu Ano,
published by Kodansha Bunko

Translation & Adaptation/Tomo Kimura
Touch-up Art & Lettering/HudsonYards
Design/Matt Hinrichs
Editor/Jonathan Tarbox

Editor in Chief, Books/Alvin Lu
Editor in Chief, Magazines/Marc Weidenbaum
VP of Publishing Licensing/Rika Inouye
VP of Sales/Gonzalo Ferreyra
Sr. VP of Marketing/Liza Coppola
Publisher/Hyoe Narita

Printed in the U.S.A.

Published by VIZ Media, LLC
P.O. Box 77010
San Francisco, CA 94107

SHONEN JUMP Manga Edition
10 9 8 7 6 5 4 3 2 1
First printing, August 2008

www.viz.com

HOSHIN ENGI

VOL. 8
THE REVOLUTION

STORY AND ART BY RYU FUJISAKI

THE CHARACTERS

NATAKU

HIKO KO

HATSU KI

SHINKOHYO

KOKUTENKO

TAIKOBO (KYOSHIGA)

SUPUSHAN

BUKICHI

The Story Thus Far

Ancient China, over 3,000 years ago. It is the era of the Yin Dynasty.

After King Chu, the emperor, married the beautiful Dakki, the good king was no longer himself, and became an unmanly and foolish ruler. Dakki, a *Sennyo* with a wicked heart, took control of Yin and the country fell into chaos.

To save the human world, the Hoshin Project was put into action. The project will seal evil Sennin and Doshi into the Shinkai, and cause Seihakuko Sho Ki to set up a new dynasty to replace Yin. Taikobo, who was chosen to execute this project, visits Sho Ki in Seiki province to encourage him to be the next king, but Sho Ki dies of illness. Hatsu Ki succeeds him and declares the province of Seiki to be "the State of Zhou," taking for himself the title King Bu. To destroy these rebels, the Maka Yonsho are sent to wreak havoc in Seiki.

VOL. 8
THE REVOLUTION

CONTENTS

Chapter 61

THE MAKA YONSHO, PART 7
TENKA RETURNS!

YOU DON'T HAVE TO READ IT, BUT SINCE THERE'S AN EXTRA PAGE:

HACK WRITING VI

- △ IT SEEMS THAT THERE ARE PEOPLE WHO "SMILE TO THEMSELVES" AND THOSE WHO DON'T.
- △ I DO.
- △ RATHER FREQUENTLY.
- △ MOREOVER, I "IMAGINE THINGS AND SMILE."
- △ THIS "IMAGINE THINGS AND SMILE" IS A PHRASE FUJISAKI CAME UP WITH (AGAIN?). AS YOU CAN TELL FROM THE EXPRESSION, YOU IMAGINE STUPID THINGS IN YOUR BRAIN AND LAUGH SOFTLY TO YOURSELF.
- △ FOR EXAMPLE, RIGHT BEFORE I WAS WRITING THIS, I WAS IMAGINING A PRIMA DONNA TURNING AROUND AND AROUND IN THE EYE OF A TYPHOON. THE PRIMA DONNA LIVES ALONE ON AN ISLAND IN THE SOUTH CHINA SEA. DURING THE TYPHOON SEASON, SHE SUDDENLY STARTS SPINNING COUNTERCLOCKWISE WITH A VENGEANCE. SHE SPINS AROUND SO MUCH, SHE RISES LIKE A HELICOPTER, AND DUE TO THE GOLDEN RULE OF THE UNIVERSE, SHE FLIES TOWARDS JAPAN...THIS IS TYPHOON NO. 1. SHE BRINGS HUGE CUMULONIMBUS CLOUDS AND A THUNDERSTORM THAT FLOODS MY HOME. SHE MOVES ON TO THE UPPER RIGHT PORTION OF THE MAP, AND THEN HER STRENGTH IS GONE. WHEN SHE STOPS SPINNING, SHE FALLS INTO THE SEA AND RETURNS TO THE ISLAND, RIDING THE CURRENT. SHE HIDES IN A DARK CAVE AND SAVES HER ENERGY, WAITING FOR HER NEXT CHANCE. SOMETIMES, SEVERAL TYPHOONS OCCUR AT ONCE. THIS IS DUE TO HER RIVAL PRIMA DONNA, "WILLY WILLY"...
- △ ...I THINK ABOUT THINGS LIKE THIS ALONE, AND SMILE.
- △ THERE SEEM TO BE PEOPLE WHO "REMEMBER THINGS AND GET MAD," BUT FUJISAKI DOESN'T DO THAT.

END OF HACK WRITING

BAM
HEH HEH HEH... THIS KONGENSAN CAN REPEL ATTACKS AS WELL AS ABSORB THEM AND STORE THEIR ENERGY...
WE MAKA YONSHO ARE *INVINCIBLE!*
RAISHINSHI!

DARN...
GAH...
THEN OUR ATTACKS ARE USELESS...
WHOMP
ROLL
WELL.
GRAB
WE NEED TO TEAR OFF THIS PAOPE.
HEY...

RIP
RIP
GWAH!
!!

THUD

HEH
...

YOU'VE PRETTY MUCH LOST YOUR LIMBS.

GLARE
WHP
FLASH

BIKIN
GNH!

REIKAI, STAY BACK. I CAN'T REPEL HIS ATTACKS VERY WELL.
ALL RIGHT.

BAM

FLAP
OON!

GAH...
GUGU

A CRACK IN THE KONGENSAN?!
WHAT THE...
CRACK
CRACK!
!!
DOES HE HAVE UNLIMITED POWER?!

CREAK CREAK
TCH...
HUFF HUFF
!
UH-OH... NATAKU'S RUNNING OUT OF POWER...
BA BAM
HE DRAINED HIMSELF TO DESTROY THE KAKOTEN...

READ
THIS
WAY

SWAY

HA

YOU'RE NOT GONNA GET AWAY WITH IT THIS EASY!
GRAB

DO IT, PAOPE HUMAN!
KILL US BOTH!
ARE YOU STUPID? DO YOU WANT TO DIE TOO?!
SHUT UP!
CLENCH
...

NO, NATAKU!
SWING

KR
ASH
AH.

I SHOULD'VE KILLED YOU.
BAM
SHUP
NOW, DIE!

!!
ZWOON

CLANK
TOO LATE!
BOOM
YOU... IDIOT...
WHAT'RE YOU DOING? GET THE UMBRELLA GUY, QUICK...
BAM

SLAM

NATAKU!

FOOLS.
THEY JUST ENDED UP BEING IN EACH OTHER'S WAY.

WELL, YOZEN, YOUR COMRADES HAVE BEEN BEATEN.
UNDO YOUR TRANSFORMA-TION! THERE'S NO NEED FOR YOUR RUSE ANYMORE!

ZZZ
ZZ
I KNEW THAT YOUR...NO, TAIKOBO'S PLAN WAS TO MAKE US FIGHT INDIVIDUALLY.
YOU THOUGHT THAT YOU COULD BEAT US ONE-ON-ONE!
HMPH... YOU UNDER-ESTIMATED US.
ZAT
MAKA YONSHO ...
...

READ
THIS
WAY

DO NOT MAKE ME ANGRY.
OTHERWISE, I WON'T BE ABLE TO CONTROL MYSELF.
KWOO

!!
SHIVER

TMP
HMPH.

DON'T TRY TO BLUFF US!
KWUN KWUN
KWUN
I'LL BURN YOU TO ASHES WITH POWER THAT MY KONGENSAN HAS ABSORBED FROM YOUR COMRADES!

STAB
STAB
?!
WHIZ
WHIZ
WHO'S THERE ?!
HMM?
OH!

I HATE TO LOSE...
I'm the dog.
GLARE
...SO I'M BACK!

封神演義

THE MAKA YONSHO, PART 8
TENKA REJOINS THE BATTLE!

TENKA ...
HAVE YOUR WOUNDS HEALED ALREADY?!
ZA
TA

READ THIS WAY

...
ALL RIGHT.

THEN I'LL FIGHT THE OTHER TWO.

YOZEN...
YOU DARE FIGHT TWO OF US MAKA YONSHO ALONE?!

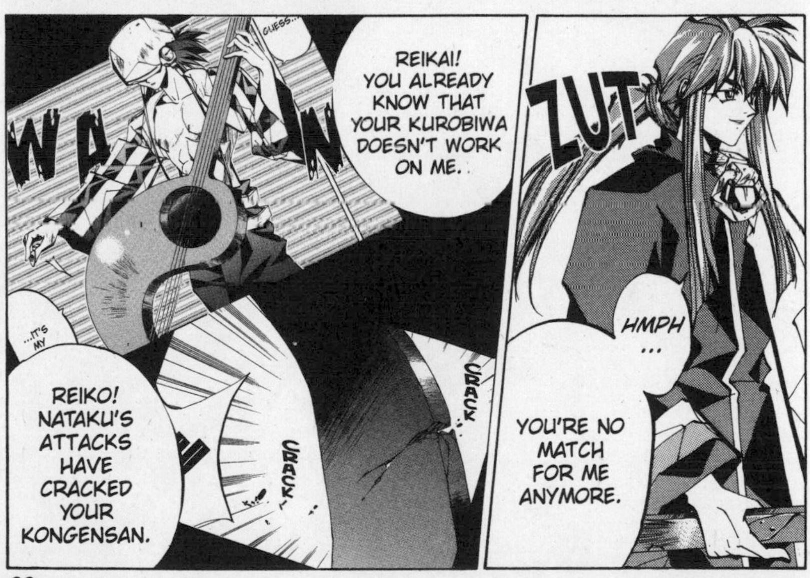
ZUT
HMPH ...
YOU'RE NO MATCH FOR ME ANYMORE.
REIKAI! YOU ALREADY KNOW THAT YOUR KUROBIWA DOESN'T WORK ON ME.
GUESS...
...IT'S MY
REIKO! NATAKU'S ATTACKS HAVE CRACKED YOUR KONGENSAN.
CRACK
CRACK

TWITCH

ALL THESE FACTORS WILL DEFEAT YOU FOR CERTAIN.

AND I HAVE MY KOTENKEN NOW.

SO, TENKA KO...

YOU CAME TO BE CUT DOWN ONCE AGAIN.
SUT

VWOM
DASH
SLAM
THIS TIME, I SHALL KILL YOU, TENKA!
VWOO

SWING

ZAZA

!!

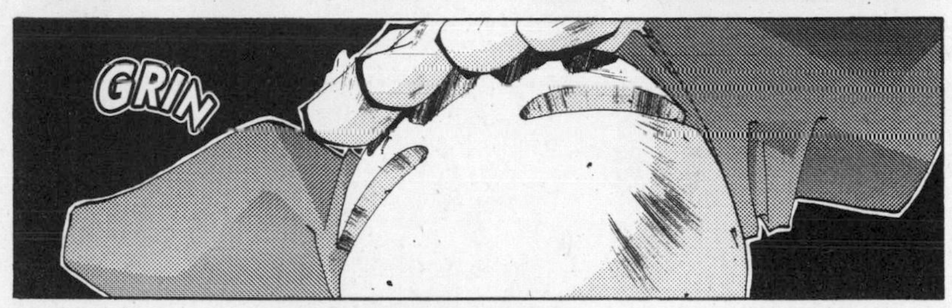

LOOK, MASTER! TENKA IS BACK!

HMM ...

YAY!

WHAT'S WRONG?! WHY WON'T YOU CELEBRATE WITH ME?

SINCE NATAKU AND RAISHINSHI CANNOT FIGHT...

I'M GLAD TENKA'S BACK...

BUT HIS WOUNDS HAVEN'T HEALED.
HE'S HANGING ON BY SHEER FORCE OF WILL.
EXACTLY!
GA GA GA G
TENKA IS FIGHTING SOLELY ON THE COMBAT SPIRIT THAT I TAUGHT HIM!
SWING
道 徳
DOTOKU SHINKUN!
TWITCH
A WARRIOR NEEDS GUTS! FIGHTING SPIRIT!
HI, TAIKOBO! HAVEN'T SEEN YOU IN A THOUSAND YEARS!
This is a lie.

Seikyo Dotoku Shinkun
One of the 12 Kongrong Elite Sennin.
Tenka's master.
He's an expert in training fighters, a Sennin full of sportsmanship.
SPORTS
SO HOW IS TENKA?
THUD
I ONLY GAVE HIM PAINKILLERS AND SEWED UP HIS WOUNDS.
IF WE 12 ELITE SENNIN INTERFERE, THE KINGO JUTTENKUN WILL JOIN THE BATTLE TOO!
THEN THE HUMAN WORLD WILL FALL INTO CHAOS! WE CAN'T LET THAT HAPPEN!
THEN WHY DON'T *YOU* FIGHT INSTEAD OF TENKA!
THE 12 ELITE SENNIN ARE ALL TALK AND NO ACTION!
I CAN'T DO THAT...
SHAKE SHAKE

YOU'RE JUST SCARED OF FIGHTING, AREN'T YOU?

ALL RIGHT, BUKICHI, LET'S ROOT FOR TENKA!

GO FOR IT, TENKA! BEAT HIM GOOD!

COACH... YOU'RE SPOILING MY WILL TO FIGHT...

HYOO HYOO

I SEE. YOU'RE USING TWO BAKUYA NO HOKEN.

HOW-EVER...

THEY'RE ONLY ENOUGH TO DEFEND YOURSELF.

GAGA

GNH!

GAGA

READ THIS WAY

SLUPT

DASH
HMPH!

OON!
SWING
BOOM

I'M SUR-PRISED...
I DIDN'T KNOW TENKA WAS SUCH A FIERY FIGHTER.

OH? I DON'T KNOW WHICH TENKA YOU'VE GOTTEN TO KNOW, TAIKOBO...
...BUT THE TENKA I KNOW IS A STRONG WARRIOR WHO'S FULL OF PASSION AND THE INSTINCT TO FIGHT!

THAT'S THE WAY HE WAS WHEN HE RE-TURNED.

I WAS DOING SOME MUSCLE TRAINING.
ONE-TWO!
ONE-TWO!
I REALLY LOVE SPORTS!

BOWOWOW

BOWOWOWOW
!

TENKA ?!

COACH... HEAL MY WOUNDS... GOTTA GET BACK...
WHAT ?!

GRIT

CLENCH
I CAN'T LOSE.
CLENCH
I WON'T LOSE...
I WON'T...

...LOSE!

HE MAY BE A BORN FIGHTER.
HE TRIES TO FIGHT EVEN WHEN THERE'S NO CHANCE OF WINNING.
I GAVE HIM ANOTHER BAKUYA NO HOKEN AND THE SANSHINTEI...

BUT I'M WORRIED THAT SOMEDAY...
THAT VERY SPIRIT MAY GET HIM KILLED.

SCATTER

CLENCH
KLANG
KLANG

THUD

MOVING TO THE SIDE WHILE THE BLADES OF THE SEIUNKEN ARE STILL THERE...

TINGLE TINGLE

I GUESS YOU'RE A BETTER SWORDSMAN THAN I AM...

FORGET IT.

YOU ONLY HAVE ONE BAKUYA NO HOKEN LEFT.

SLIC
YOU KNOW YOU CAN'T WARD OFF MY ATTACKS WITH JUST ONE SWORD.
WARD OFF YOUR ATTACKS?
SWING
GIIN
?!

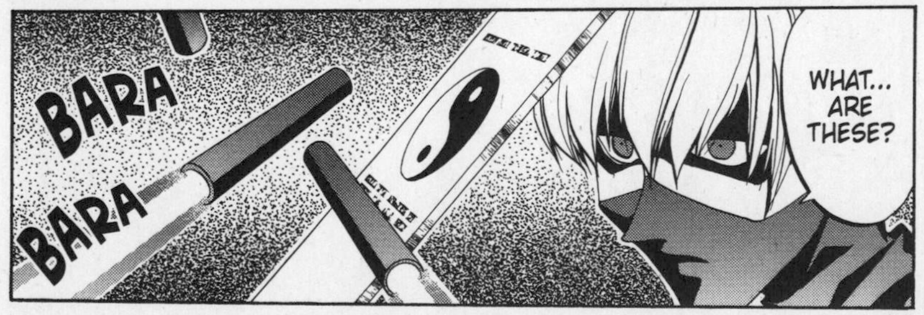
WHAT... ARE THESE?
BARA
BARA

WHIZ
YAH!
VWM
I DON'T NEED TO DODGE YOUR ATTACKS...
I'LL GET YOU WITH THE PAOPE SANSHINTEI!
DODGE
HMPH ...
WHAT CAN YOU DO WITH A PAOPE YOU'RE NOT USED TO WIELDING?!

THUD
WHA...
WHAT?

NO...
IT CAN'T BE!

B-AM

GAH... YOU USED REIKO'S KONGENSAN...
COLLAPSE
...TO SHOOT THEM BACK AT ME!

SIGH.
YOU WERE A PRETTY TOUGH FIGHTER.

封神演義

OOO

CHAPTER 63: THE MAKA YONSHO, PART 9 THE ORIGINAL FORM OF THE MAKA YONSHO

CREAK

YEAH, TENKA! WAY TO GO!

DASH

HEY!

OUCH!

BANG

WHOA!

FLAP

FLAP

HEY ...

G-GET OUT OF THE WAY!

OOO

Chapter 63

THE MAKA YONSHO, PART 9
THE ORIGINAL FORM OF THE MAKA YONSHO

MAREI-
SEI...
VWM
I'LL DEAL YOU THE FINAL BLOW!
...
GRIN
HA
TENKA, WATCH OUT!

SMASH

ZAT
REIJU... IS REISEI ALL RIGHT?!
HE DODGED IT. HE'S NOT SLOW ENOUGH TO BE CRUSHED.
SWAY
SEE?
REIKO, REIKAI, REIJU...

WE MUST DO IT NOW...
WE'LL REVERT TO OUR ORIGINAL FORM AND KILL EVERY ONE OF THE KONGRONG SENNIN, ALONG WITH THIS CITY!

...
ARE YOU ALL RIGHT, TENKA?!

BUT WHAT ABOUT DAD AND THE OTHERS? THEY'RE STILL UP THERE!

DON'T WORRY.

PAT

YOUR MASTER IS CARRYING DOWN NATAKU AND RAISHINSHI WITH HIS KOKIN RIKISHI.

THE BUSEIO IS ALREADY ON GROUND.

GWOO

NOW, KOTENKEN.

GO!

GWOOO

AM

OOO
MOUTH
OOO
WH

WH... WHAT'S WITH THAT DOG?!
IT TOOK OUT THE WHALE LIKE IT WAS NOTHING!
YOZEN, YOU JERK...
WHY DIDN'T HE DO THIS EARLIER?!

IT'S BECAUSE YOU GUYS WERE FIGHTING ON THE KAKOTEN!
THAT'S WHY THE BUSEIO DIDN'T KILL MAREIJU, EITHER!
SPORTS!

BUT WHY?!
YOU'VE GOT A POINT THERE...
IF HE GOT THE WHALE, HE COULD'VE KILLED THE MAKA YONSHO WHO WERE ON IT!
TAIKOBO... IT LOOKED AS IF YOZEN WAS FIGHTING WITHOUT *ACTUALLY TRYING TO KILL* THE MAKA YONSHO...
KABOOM
BOOM

YOZEN KNEW...

...THAT HE NEEDED TO WEAKEN THE MAKA YONSHO WHILE THEY WERE STILL IN HUMAN FORM.

THE MAKA YONSHO ARE YOKAI SENNIN.

OKIJIN, WHO WAS ALSO A YOKAI SENNIN, RETURNED TO HER ORIGINAL FORM WHEN I DEFEATED HER IN HER HUMAN FORM.

OKIJIN'S ORIGINAL FORM WAS A STONE LUTE. THE MAKA YONSHO SEEM TO BE DIFFERENT.

THEY EXHIBIT THEIR TRUE STRENGTH WHEN THEY'RE BACK IN THEIR ORIGINAL FORM.

KRASH
SSH

GWOOOOOOO
I DIDN'T THINK THEY'D BE THIS STRONG...
THEY'LL GET THIS KAKOTEN SOON...

WE CANNOT AFFORD TO BE WOUNDED ANYMORE IN OUR HUMAN FORM...
WE'D BETTER RETURN TO OUR ORIGINAL FORM QUICKLY!

KA WHAP

FLASH

WH... WHAT'S GOING ON?
THE WHALE'S GONE.

DASH
UH, YOZEN, WHERE'RE YOU GOING?!
THEY'RE FINALLY BACK IN THEIR ORIGINAL FORM...

...AS YOKAI!
GOGOGO

READ THIS WAY

OOOOOO
WHOA!
WHAT IS *THAT*, MASTER?!

IT'S A FOUR-HEADED LEGENDARY BEAST CALLED SHO.
LOOKS LIKE THAT IS THE MAKA YONSHO'S ORIGINAL FORM.

THAT'S MAREISEI'S ATTACK!

IT HAS ABSORBED THE ABILITIES OF THEIR PAOPE!

GIGIGIIN

THEN IT'S INVINCIBLE!

OUR ATTACKS WILL BE REPELLED BY MAREIKO'S UMBRELLA!

READ
THIS
WAY

TWANG
WAH!
BUKICHI!

THROB
IS THIS MAREIKAI'S BIWA LUTE?

My head hurts!
HURRY UP, YOZEN!

DASH

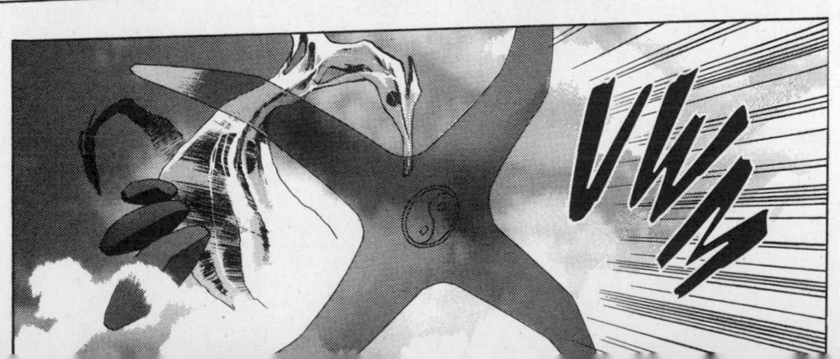

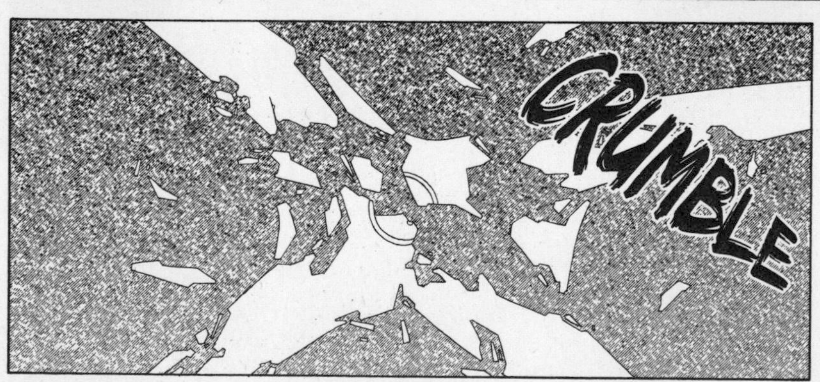
CRUMBLE

BAM
HMPH... I TOLD YOU THAT NATAKU'S ATTACKS HAD CRACKED THE KONGENSAN.
STOMP
BESIDES ...
THUNK
...THE BAD GUY WHO BECOMES A MONSTER AS A LAST RESORT IS BOUND TO LOSE!

封神演義

Chapter 64

THE MAKA YONSHO, PART 10
THE MAKA YONSHO ARE SENT TO THE HOSHINDAI

OOO
WHOA!
YOZEN DID IT!
BUBBLE
BUBBLE
!

RORORO...

ROT AWAY!

YOZEN! DEAL THE FINAL BLOW NOW!

SWAY

NO!

THESE GUYS ARE DREADFUL ...

THEY MEAN TO ROT AWAY THE EARTH OF HOYU TO AVENGE THEIR DEATHS!

HUH?

ATTACKS WITH MY SANSENTO WILL NOT REACH THAT FAR AWAY.

OOO

OOO

AND I DO NOT WANT TO USE MY KOTENKEN AGAINST A FILTHY THING LIKE THAT.

THIS IS NO TIME TO MOAN ABOUT THE DETAILS!

TAIKOBO SUSU!

IN THIS BATTLE, WE DOSHI OF KONGRONG FOUGHT TOGETHER FOR THE FIRST TIME.

WE MADE AMAZING PROGRESS.

THAT IS WHY...

CLINK

!

...*YOU* MUST BRING THINGS TO A CLOSE.

...
ALL RIGHT.
SLAP
BA-BUMP
BUT, YOZEN... IF THEY MOVE AND ATTACK AGAIN...
BA-BUMP
THEY DON'T HAVE THAT SORT OF POWER LEFT! NOW STRAIGHTEN YOUR BACK!

A-ALL RIGHT...
CLICK

GWOOO
YAH!

SLAM
道徳
FLASH
BOOM

WELL...
IT'S OVER!
SIGH
ARE YOU...
...REALLY RAISHINSHI?
HUFF
CLENCH

GLAD TO HAVE YOU BACK.

GRIN

READ THIS WAY
TEARS
FATHER!

FATHER?

YOU TWIT! I'M HATSU KI!
LITTLE BIG BROTHER?! HOW COME YOU'RE SO BIG NOW?!
FOOL! YOU KNOW HOW MANY YEARS YOU'VE BEEN GONE?!

TAIKOBO!
BOOM

SPORTS!!
NATAKU'S BROKEN!
LET'S HAVE TAIITSU FIX HIM!

PSSS
BEEP
GA GA GA
YEP, HE'S BROKEN...

BY THE WAY, BUKICHI...
YES SIR!

HEY! WHAT THE HELL'S GOING ON?!

PAT
HAND
WOULD YOU LIKE TO TRAIN UNDER ME? YOU CAN AIM FOR THE STARS WITH THOSE LEGS!
YOU IDIOT...

READ THIS WAY

THE GROUND IS *ROTTING!*
GWOOO
NAN KYUKATSU ...
THOSE YOKAI SENNIN REALLY TICK ME OFF!

THEN A THOUSAND OF US WILL GO AGAINST THEM!
PAOO
THUM
GAH!
THUM
THE SENNIN OF KINGO CAUSE NOTHING BUT TROUBLE FOR US.
PAOO
THE PEOPLE OF ZHOU SUFFERED GREATLY THIS TIME.
IF THEY'RE GOING TO GET US, LET US PREPARE TO DIE...
...AND DEFEAT THE SOURCE OF ALL THIS, DAKKI AND BUNCHU...AND TSUTEN KYOSHU, WHO'S BACKING THEM UP!

HOWEVER... I WANT TO MINIMIZE CASUALTIES.

THIS MAY BE THE ARROGANCE OF A DOSHI...

DON'T WORRY ABOUT IT TOO MUCH, TAIKOBO!
YOU'VE GOT PLENTY OF ALLIES!
BWA HA HA HA
WE CAN ALL FIGHT TOGETHER!
HMM...
MASTER!
ZOOM

ZOOOOOM
I'M BACK!
SUPU! ARE YOU ALL RIGHT?!
HAKUTSURU TOOK CARE OF ME. I'M FINE NOW!
SO, MASTER, WHERE'RE THOSE ENEMIES?!
I'M READY TO FIGHT!
GLARE
SIGH

Choka

EVEN THE MAKA YONSHO WERE SEALED...

THINGS WOULD BE OVER QUICKLY IF I HAD GONE MYSELF...
THE SENNIN OF KONGRONG ARE BECOMING STRONGER WITH EVERY BATTLE.

SHIVER TREMBLE
BUT SINCE HIS MAJESTY KING CHU IS IN THIS CONDITION...

LORD BUNCHU!
KINGO ISLAND HAS SENT AN ENVOY!

AN ENVOY?
SPARKLE
SPARKLE

BUNCHU!
TADA
LONG TIME NO SEE!
CHOKOMEI!
OH, I MUST FIRST RELAY LORD TSUTEN KYOSHU'S MESSAGE TO YOU...
FWIP
Secret message

BUNCHU! LORD TSUTEN KYOSHU GRANTS YOU THE RIGHT OF COMMAND OVER ALL SENNIN OF KINGO ISLAND!
THEREFORE, YOU'LL BE ABLE TO USE THE KINGO JUTTENKUN AS WELL!

THE JUTTEN-KUN!

HIS BIDDING IS TO USE THOSE FORCES TO ASSIST YIN AND TO DESTROY THE KONGRONG MOUNTAINS!

SHUP
SHUP
AND...

...OF COURSE, I MYSELF SHALL JOIN THIS BATTLE!

POP POP

POP POP

I WILL BE YOUR GUEST IN THIS CASTLE...

...YES?

LOOM

FOOTNOTE: FLOWERED PICTURED ABOVE IS LILIUM AURATUM

封神演義

YOU DON'T HAVE TO READ IT, BUT SINCE THERE'S AN EXTRA PAGE:

HACK WRITING VII

△ THE OTHER DAY, I WENT TO THE PARASITE MUSEUM IN MEGURO, TOKYO.

△ I DON'T HAVE A THING FOR PARASITES, OR LIKE THEM BECAUSE THEY'RE WHITE. ACTUALLY, I THINK I HATE THEM. BUT I'VE ALWAYS WANTED TO GO TO A MUSEUM THAT DISPLAYS ALL KINDS OF PARASITES. PERHAPS MY SUBCONSCIOUS DROVE ME TO GO THERE.

△ IT TAKES QUITE A WHILE JUST TO ***GET THERE***.

△ I RODE THE TRAIN FOR ABOUT 45 MINUTES TO GET TO MEGURO. THEN I HAD TO WALK ON A ROAD THAT GOES UP AND DOWN FOR ABOUT 15 MINUTES.

△ I PLODDED AWAY, MAP IN HAND, MAKING SURE I WAS ON THE RIGHT ROAD.

△ I WAS TRUDGING ALONG A ROAD THAT GENTLY WENT UP AND DOWN, WHEN I NOTICED THAT THE BUILDINGS IN THE CITY ALL LOOKED ALIKE. THERE MUST BE CITIES LIKE THIS ALL OVER JAPAN. SOMEONE DESIGNED IT, SOMEONE TRANSPORTED THE BUILDING MATERIALS AND BUILT A CITY ***HERE***. BUT IF YOU STRAIN YOUR EYES, YOU CAN FIND THE PARASITE MUSEUM. IT IS BURIED AMONG OTHER BUILDINGS, AND A CARELESS PERSON MIGHT OVERLOOK IT. BUT IF YOU LOOK CAREFULLY ENOUGH, ANYBODY CAN FIND THAT MEDIOCRE BUILDING.

△ I WENT IN, MY HEART POUNDING.

△ SEVERAL PEOPLE WERE ALREADY INSIDE, LOOKING AT THE PARASITES IN THE GLASS CASES. THERE WERE ALL SORTS OF PEOPLE, FROM HIGH SCHOOL STUDENTS TO SENIOR CITIZENS. AND THEY WERE EARNESTLY STARING AT THE PARASITES FROM VERY CLOSE, AS IF THEY'D BECOME ONE WITH THE PARASITES. THAT SCARED ME A LITTLE, BUT SOON I GOT USED TO IT AND WENT UP TO THE SECOND FLOOR (THE MUSEUM OCCUPIES THE FIRST AND SECOND FLOORS OF THIS BUILDING). OF COURSE, THERE WERE PEOPLE ON THE SECOND FLOOR TOO, BUT WHAT CAUGHT MY EYE WAS NOT THE VISITORS, BUT THE PARASITE DISPLAYED BEHIND THEM. IT LOOKED LIKE A FIRE HOSE...AND IT'S DISPLAYED AT THE HEART OF THE PARASITE MUSEUM. IT WAS A REALLY PRIMITIVE, ***FLAT NOODLE***-LIKE, HUMONGOUS DIPHYLLBOTHRIUM.

△ THERE WAS NO ONE AROUND IT, SO I WAS ABLE TO LOOK AT IT AS MUCH I WANTED. BUT THE MORE I TRIED TO LOOK AT IT, THE MORE SHAPELESS IT BECAME AND DISAPPEARED. I BECAME A LITTLE SAD AND LEFT. THEN, I SPENT AN HOUR GETTING BACK HOME.

△ THIS IS MY OWN PERSONAL OPINION, AND THE REALITY MAY BE DIFFERENT. HOWEVER, THE PARASITE MUSEUM DOES EXIST. WHY DON'T YOU GO VISIT IT YOURSELF?

END OF HACK WRITING

Chapter 65

MISSION: IMPOSSIBLE!

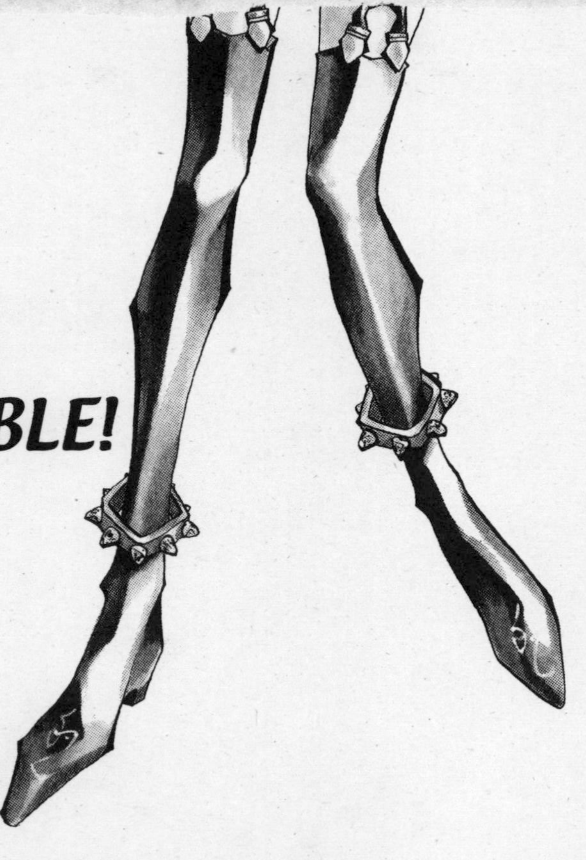

CHAPTER 65 MISSION: IMPOSSIBLE!

YOU FOOLS!

BOOM

OOOO
PANT
PANT
CHOKOMEI... I TOLD YOU TO LEAVE THE OTHER DAY...
GAGAGAGA

I HOPE YOU APPRECIATE WHAT'LL HAPPEN...

SWOOSH

...IF THIS TAISHI BUNCHU BECOMES YOUR *ENEMY!*

COMPARED TO THE SENDO OF KONGRONG, WE OF KINGO...

...RATHER LACK SOLIDARITY, DON'T YOU THINK?

READ THIS WAY

MEANWHILE, TAIKOBO IN ZHOU...

I'VE NEVER SEEN YOU THIS BUSY, MASTER.
WHAT'RE YOU DOING?

REMEMBER WHAT HAPPENED WHEN WE FOUGHT THE MAKA YONSHO.
CHOMP CHOMP CHOMP
IF WE STAY IN THE CITY, THE PEOPLE MAY GET HURT AGAIN.

WE NEED TO BUILD A FORTRESS.
A FOR-TRESS?

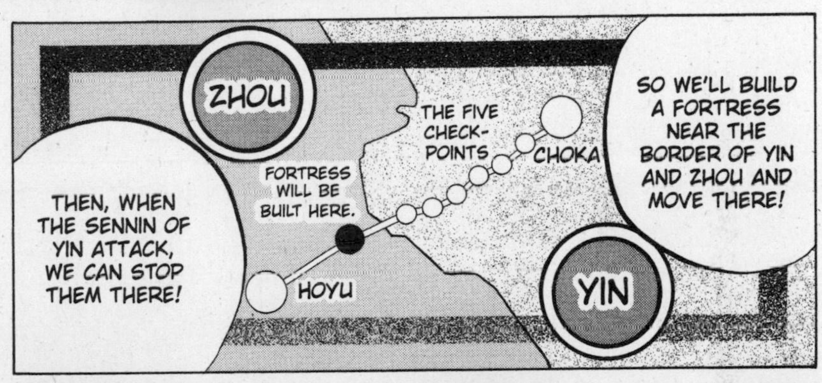
SO WE'LL BUILD A FORTRESS NEAR THE BORDER OF YIN AND ZHOU AND MOVE THERE!
ZHOU
THE FIVE CHECK-POINTS
CHOKA
FORTRESS WILL BE BUILT HERE.
HOYU
YIN
THEN, WHEN THE SENNIN OF YIN ATTACK, WE CAN STOP THEM THERE!

I'VE ALREADY SENT YOZEN OVER TO SUPERVISE THINGS.
Twitch

?
SOME-THING WRONG, BUKICHI?
SOMEONE'S WATCHING US!

DARN!
ALL RIGHT!
FLASH
GO, GOKOSEKI!
DID THEY SEE ME ?!
WH

WHAM

OH NO...

HEY!
DASH
MASTER!
SLAP
MASTER!
BA BAM

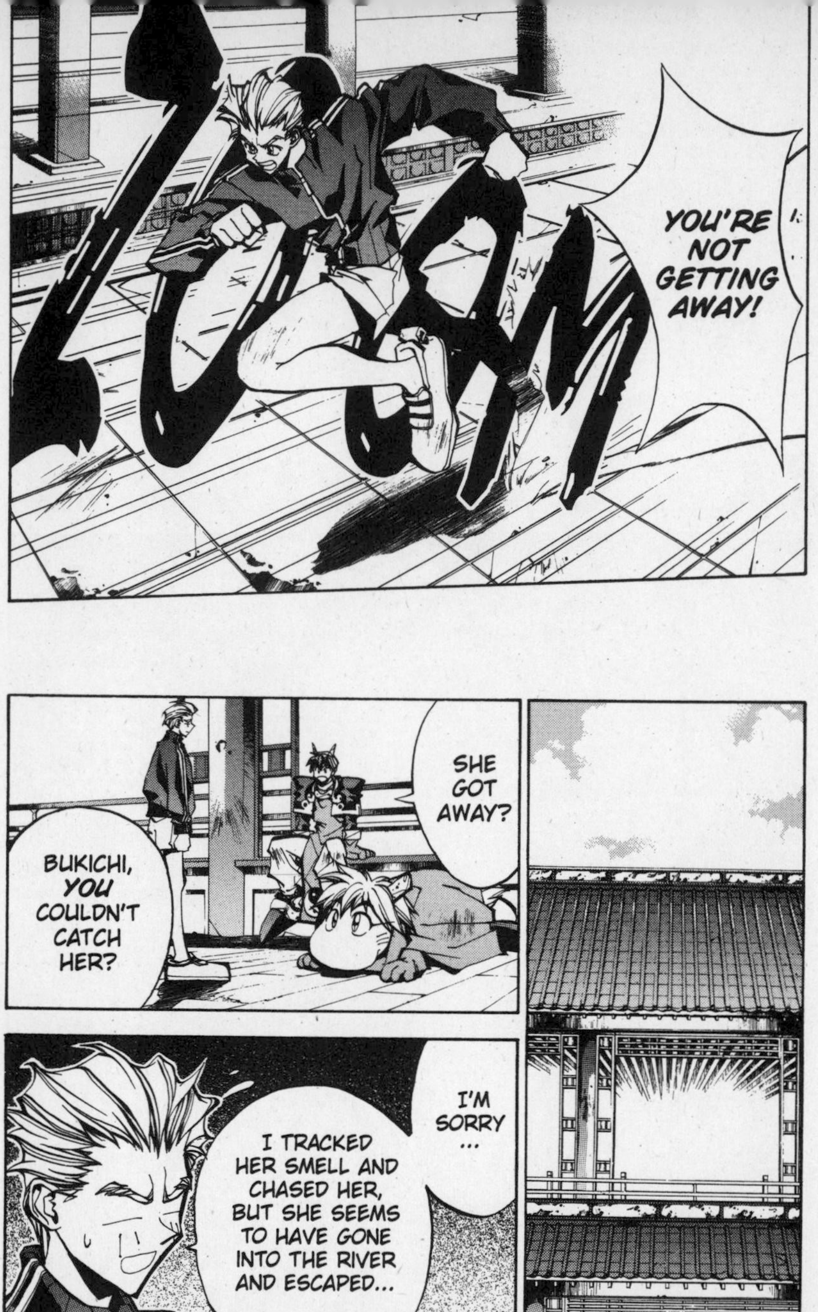

YOU'RE NOT GETTING AWAY!

SHE GOT AWAY?

BUKICHI, *YOU* COULDN'T CATCH HER?

I'M SORRY ...

I TRACKED HER SMELL AND CHASED HER, BUT SHE SEEMS TO HAVE GONE INTO THE RIVER AND ESCAPED...

WELL, ALL RIGHT.
SHE'S PROBABLY A DOSHI.

A DOSHI ?!

THE STONE SHE THREW IS A PAOPE.
五光石

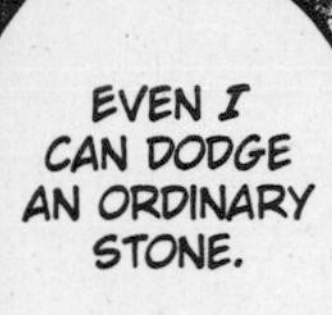
EVEN I CAN DODGE AN ORDINARY STONE.

IS SHE OUR ENEMY, MASTER?
DUNNO ...

WE'VE GOT TO FIND OUT WHO SHE IS!
WILL YOU TWO INVESTIGATE?

YES SIR!
ROGER!

HOOOOWL

CAN'T FIND HER...
SHE'S NOT AROUND ANY-WHERE...

MASTER?
WHY'S HE LOOKING AROUND?
GLANCE
GLANCE

BUT SHE MIGHT BE OUR ENEMY. I'VE *GOT* TO FIND HER SOMEHOW...
HUH?

OH, NO!
CHOMP
CHOMP
MASTER'S STEALING PEACHES FROM THE CASTLE WAREHOUSE LATE AT NIGHT!

READ THIS WAY

OH NO...

OOPS...

WHAM
AAAAH!

!!
WHO ARE YOU?!
OOO
GOOD JOB, SUPU-SHAN!
DASH
HEH... HEH HEH HEH...
SHP
ALL RIGHT, THEN...

I'M A SPY!
TADA
I'M THE LOVELY TOH SENGYOKU, WHO GATHERS INTELLIGENCE ABOUT ZHOU UNDER THE ORDERS OF BUN TAISHI!

封神演義

CHAPTER 66: THE BIRDS

I WONDER IF HE'S CHANGED HIS WAYS?

GUMO

GUMO

Chapter 66
THE BIRDS

READ THIS WAY

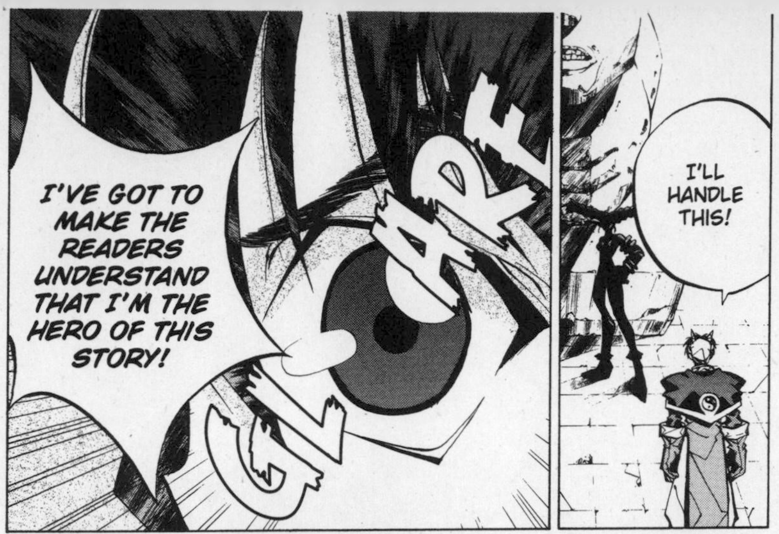
I'LL HANDLE THIS!
I'VE GOT TO MAKE THE READERS UNDERSTAND THAT I'M THE HERO OF THIS STORY!
GLARE

WHA...
YOU'RE THE HERO?!
GASP
SIGH...SEE? NATAKU AND YOZEN ALWAYS BUTT IN WHEN WE FIGHT...

EVEN THOUGH YOU'RE A SPY, YOU WENT OUT OF YOUR WAY TO ATTRACT ATTENTION SO WE'D NOTICE YOU, RIGHT?
GASP
I DON'T KNOW WHAT YOU'RE TALKING ABOUT!
BINGO.

BUT I CAN'T AFFORD TO HAVE ADDITIONAL SUPPORTING PLAYERS!
MASTER...
SHAKE SHAKE
SUPUSHAN!
YOU'RE COCKY WHEN YOUR OPPONENT IS A GIRL. I'M ASHAMED OF YOU...
COLLAPSE
HYOO
YOU SPY! I'LL GET YOU WITH MY DASHINBEN!
HMPH... ALL RIGHT...
YOU'RE GOING TO FIGHT ME WHEN I'M INVINCIBLE?!

YOU HAVE NO IDEA HOW TERRIFYING MY PAOPE GOKOSEKI IS!

TAKE THIS! DREAM BALL NO. 3!

I CAN DODGE THAT!

FWOOSH

WHIZ

WAH!

BEND

WHAM

BEND

OH NOOOO...

MASTER!
WHAM
HEH...
ZAT

HEY, HEY, DID YOU SEE THAT?
THIS PAOPE **ALWAYS** HITS THE TARGET!
HEH HEH

FLASH
AND WHAT'S EVEN WORSE...
SPARKLE
...THE FACE OF WHOEVER GETS HIT TURNS *WEIRDLY EROTIC!*
WHAT A STUPID PAOPE!
SWAT
TAIKOBO.
ZAT
YOU HAVEN'T CHANGED AT ALL.
GAGAGAT
!
STUPID?! YOU DARE CALL IT STUPID?!
AAAA

SU KOKUKO ?!

HMM?

TWITCH

GUMO GUMO

GUMO GUMO

OH NO! YOU'VE GOT BACKUP!
EVEN I CAN'T FIGHT ALL OF YOU AT ONCE!

I'LL GET YOU LATER, TAIKOBO!
ZOOM

AHA.
GRIN
GUMO
WHO'S THAT GIRL, TAIKOBO?

UH...ANYWAY, SU KOKUKO, WHY HAVE YOU COME TO HOYU?
WELL...

BECAUSE WE'RE READY NOW.

READY?

READ THIS WAY

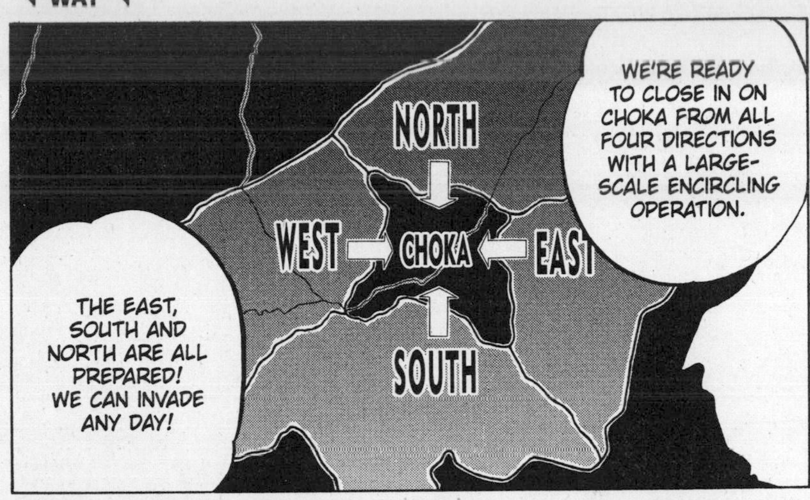
WE'RE READY TO CLOSE IN ON CHOKA FROM ALL FOUR DIRECTIONS WITH A LARGE-SCALE ENCIRCLING OPERATION.
NORTH
WEST
CHOKA
EAST
SOUTH
THE EAST, SOUTH AND NORTH ARE ALL PREPARED! WE CAN INVADE ANY DAY!

I SEE...
BUT THERE'RE NO SENDO IN THE SOUTH AND EAST.

SO, I'LL GO ASK LORD GENSHI TENSON TO SEND US SOME HELP.
WE NEED SENNIN TO FIGHT THE SENNIN OF YIN.

INDEED!

GOOD...
HE'S LEAVING...

LETTER OF CHALLENGE
SPY, THE TIME HAS COME TO FIGHT IT OUT.
I'LL WAIT FOR YOU AT THE CENTRAL PLAZA OF HOYU CASTLE TOMORROW AT NOON. IF YOU WIN, YOU CAN SPY AS YOU WISH. IF I WIN, YOU LEAVE AT ONCE!

HEH HEH HEH...
HAA HAHAHAHA. ALL RIGHT!
I GUESS A SPY HAS GOTTA ACCEPT A CHALLENGE!

The Next Day
mrmr
mrmr

WOO!

WHA...

WHAT'RE ALL THESE PEOPLE DOING HERE?!

Go for it, spy!

I'LL PROVE MY TALENT AS A SPY...

I'M SORRY, MISS SPY.

THE PEOPLE OF ZHOU LOVE FESTIVALS, SO SOMEHOW THEY ALWAYS FIND OUT WHEN SOMETHING'S GOING ON.

WELL, THAT'S ALL RIGHT.

...TO ALL THESE IDIOTS!

PUDDING! ♡

GRAB

KYAAAAAAAH!

READ THIS WAY

TIME FOR OUR DUEL!

READ THIS WAY

MASTER, WHY'RE YOU WEARING A BIRD SUIT?
HEH HEH HEH. DID I SURPRISE YOU, SUPU?
I'M MORE APPALLED THAN SURPRISED...

THIS SPY HATES BIRDS!
WING
I NOTICED SHE LOST HER COOL WHEN SHE SAW SHIN'YO THE OTHER DAY!

NO... NO...
DON'T GET ANY CLOSER!
SHIVER
SHIVER

HAA HA HA HA HA!
FLAP
FLAP.
NOOOOOOOOOOO!

H-HE'S FLYING?!

FLAP

FLAP

OH NO!

A DEAD END!

HE'S GOT THE DASHINBEN IN HIS WINGS.

ZAT

KAA!!

NOOOO!

SNAP

STAY AWAY FROM ME, SCUM-BAG!

KA WHAM

封神演義

Chapter 67

THE REVOLUTION BEGINS!

SO DO YOU UNDERSTAND, KING BU? TOMORROW WE'LL TELL THE PEOPLE THAT WE'RE GOING TO START THE WAR.
MEMORIZE THE SPEECH THAT I WROTE.

READ THIS WAY

BY THE WAY, TAIKOBO AND THE OTHERS SEEM SO BUSY. WHAT'S GOING ON?

THE WAR AGAINST YIN...

KING BU IS GOING TO OFFICIALLY DECLARE WAR AGAINST YIN TOMORROW.
WE'LL HAVE THOUSANDS OF PEOPLE GATHER AT THE PLAZA FOR THIS.

SILLY! I'M WORKING FOR YIN! THERE'S NO WAY YOU GUYS CAN WIN!
BWA HA HA
SHE KNOWS EVERYTHING...

The Next Day

RUB
RUB

KYUUN
BE STILL, KOTENKEN.
RUB
RUB
TODAY'S AN IMPORTANT DAY, SO I'VE GOT TO GET YOU CLEANED UP!

YOZEN!
TAIKOBO SUSU...

SO NATAKU, TENKA AND RAISHINSHI CAN'T MAKE IT?
NO.

THEIR WOUNDS ARE STILL SERIOUS.
IT WILL TAKE QUITE SOME TIME FOR THEM TO GET WELL.
RIP
BAM
STAB

READ THIS WAY

BUT I'M MORE THAN ENOUGH TO REPRESENT THE SENNIN WORLD.
HMPH
UH... OKAY...

AH, TAIKOBO! THERE YOU ARE!
TMP
TMP

WE CAME IN PLACE OF NATAKU AND THE OTHER TWO.
ZAT
YOU'LL NEED PLENTY OF SENNIN TO MARK THIS GLORIOUS OCCASION!

THE MAD SCIENTIST, THE SPORTS NUT AND THE WEIRDO. THE THREE ECCENTRICS!
DON'T LUMP ME TOGETHER WITH THESE TWO.

BY THE WAY, YOZEN...

HEH HEH HEH. I'M NOT GOING TO LET YOU STEAL THE SHOW.
LORD TAIITSU SHINJIN, THANK YOU FOR HONORING US WITH YOUR PRESENCE.

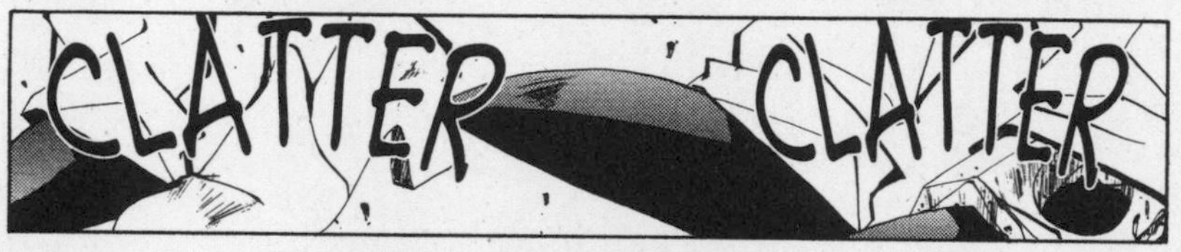
CLATTER
CLATTER

UGH, I'M GETTING NERVOUS. AS BUSEIO, I'VE GOTTA MAKE A SPEECH, TOO.
UM, TODAY'S AN AUSPICIOUS DAY...
CLATTER
FATHER, BUY ME SOME FRIED NOODLES.
IS MY TIE STRAIGHT?
CLATTER
I WILL TALK ABOUT POLITICS AND ECONOMICS.
GET YOUR ACT TOGETHER, HIKO KO!
CLATTER

LOOKS LIKE THEY'RE HAVING FUN.
WOULD YOU LIKE TO ATTEND, TOO?
OH, I COULDN'T ...I'M YOUR ENEMY!
BUT IF YOU INSIST, I'LL ATTEND!

READ THIS WAY

AMBLE
AMBLE
Seiki Castle

LISTEN, KING BU. FIFTY THOUSAND PEOPLE ARE WAITING BEYOND THIS DOOR.
GIVE IT YOUR BEST!

GOT IT! HERE GOES!

AND GIVE YOUR SPEECH INTO THIS.
TAIITSU MADE THIS FOR TODAY. IT'S A MICROPHONE.

CREAK

OOO
OOO

DWOO

OOO

UH...
...WARS ARE GOOD FOR NOTHING!
DAMN... THAT IDIOT!
THAT'S NOT WHAT I WROTE!
BUT I'VE DECIDED TO FIGHT AGAINST YIN.
I CAN'T ALLOW A TYRANT TO DO AS HE PLEASES ANYMORE. I'VE HAD ENOUGH.

I DON'T HAVE THE TALENTS OF MY FATHER SHO KI OR BIG BROTHER HAKUYUKO, BUT WITH YOUR SUPPORT, WE CAN PREVAIL.

SO I ASK YOU PEOPLE TO FOLLOW ME!

...

Choka

LORD BUNCHU! WE HAVE TROUBLE!
CLATTER CLATTER
WHAT IS IT, CHOKEI?
ACCORDING TO OUR INTELLIGENCE DEPARTMENT, A RALLY WAS HELD IN ZHOU!
TAIKOBO WILL BE INVADING CHOKA, LEADING ZHOU'S SOLDIERS!

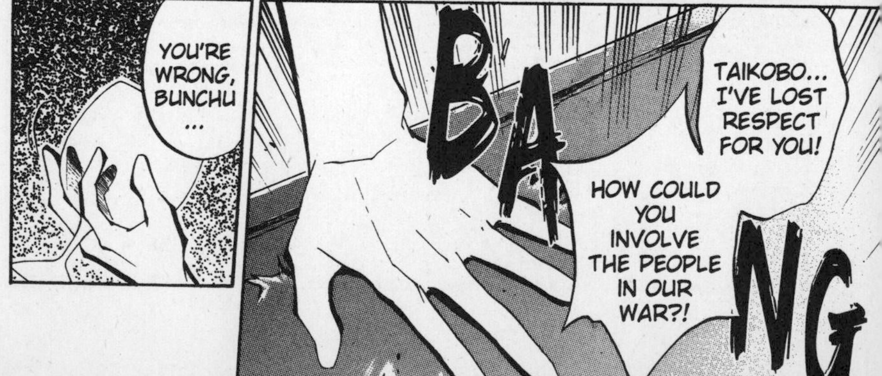
TAIKOBO... I'VE LOST RESPECT FOR YOU!
HOW COULD YOU INVOLVE THE PEOPLE IN OUR WAR?!
BANG
YOU'RE WRONG, BUNCHU ...

READ THIS WAY

TAIKOBO *COULDN'T HELP* DOING SO.
THE ANTICS OF THE MAKA YONSHO DESTROYED HOYU...IT'S ONLY NATURAL THAT THE PEOPLE NOW THIRST FOR WAR.

I'M NOT GOING TO CATER TO YOUR WHIMS!
I *WON'T* USE THE PEOPLE! I JUST NEED TO USE THE JUTTENKUN TO DEFEAT THE SENNIN OF KONGRONG AND DAKKI!

PERHAPS YOU SHOULD GIVE UP AND FIGHT A LARGE-SCALE WAR USING HUMANS?
A MAGNIFICENT AND GORGEOUS WAR...OOH... HOW LOVELY.

NOT USE THE PEOPLE? I'M AFRAID THAT'S IMPOSSIBLE.
DOINK
LOOK BEYOND THE KINRANDEN!

?!
THAT'S...

WAH!
LADY DAKKI!
LADY DAKKI!
様
LADY DAKKI!

GIGGLE. ♡

WINK

DAKKI
OOOH, LADY DAKKI!
LADY DAKKI, I'M SO HAPPY!

TWIST
PLEASE LISTEN, EVERYBODY. ♡
I'M SAYING THIS ON BEHALF OF KING CHU, WHO IS ILL. ♡
THE FEUDAL LORDS OF THE EAST, WEST, SOUTH AND NORTH ARE ABOUT TO INVADE CHOKA...

WHAT'S GOING ON?!
DAKKI GATHERED HALF A MILLION PEOPLE USING HER TEMPTATION JUTSU.

HALF A MIL-LION?!
DAKKI HAS BECOME THAT POWERFUL?!

OH NO! DAKKI DOESN'T KNOW WHAT TO DO! ♡
NO NO!
HELP ME! ♡
WAH
LADY DAKKI!
LADY DAKKI!
LADY DAKKI!
BEAUTY

READ
THIS
WAY

ZAT
YOU FOX!
HOW COULD YOU STIR UP THE PEOPLE LIKE THIS?!

DIDN'T YOU PROMISE TO BEHAVE FOR A WHILE?!
OH? ♡ I DIDN'T PROMISE ANYTHING IN WRITING. ♡

COME ON, WE'LL JUST MAKE THE HUMANS FIGHT EACH OTHER. ♡
AND WE'LL MANIPULATE THEM BEHIND THE SCENES... JUST LIKE TAIKOBO. ♡

JUST LIKE TAIKOBO?!
AT LEAST TAIKOBO CARES FOR THE PEOPLE! YOU'RE JUST PLAYING AROUND!

GIGGLE. ♡
IS THAT SO?

HEH HEH HEH. LOOK AT THAT, KOKUTENKO.
SENDO ARE ABOUT TO CHANGE THE HISTORY OF THIS COUNTRY.

YOU DON'T MIND, SHINKOHYO?
WON'T THINGS BE OVER IF YOU DEFEAT DAKKI YOURSELF?

I CAN'T DO THAT.
POINT BLANK
WHY NOT?
I JUST CAN'T.

11th Century B.C., Ancient China

THE ZHOU ARMY—50 THOUSAND SOLDIERS. THE YIN ARMY—700 THOUSAND SOLDIERS. THIS REVOLUTIONARY WAR BEGAN WITH YIN HAVING AN OVERWHELMING ADVANTAGE.

封神演義

THE INSIDE OF KINGO ISLAND

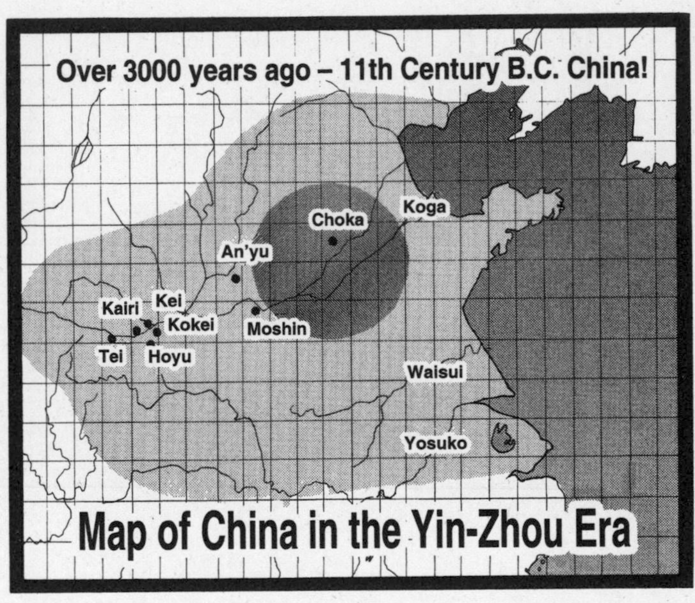

YIN AND ZHOU BOTH DECIDED TO HAVE SENNIN AND HUMANS FIGHT TOGETHER IN A COALITION.

ZHOU APPOINTED THE GENERAL TAIKOBO AND YIN APPOINTED THE TAISHI BUNCHU AS COMMANDERS TO FIGHT THIS HISTORIC WAR.

Meanwhile, Bunchu in Yin...

Choka,
the Royal Capital
The Forbidden Palace
6:00 P.M.

BUT LORD BUN-CHU!

TAIKOBO IS ADVANCING USING HIS SOLDIERS, FAIR AND SQUARE!

FIGHTING THEM USING THE JUTTENKUN IS...

CLAP

CLAP

CLAP

CLAP

!

UNFAIR, CHOKEI?

BUT THIS IS MY STRATEGY! SENDO CAUSED THIS WAR, AND I WANT TO MINIMIZE THE CASUALTIES!

TADA

WHO IS IT?!

BRAVO!
I BELIEVE THAT STRATEGY IS MORE IMPORTANT THAN TACTICS IN A WAR!
SAA
READERS! USE A DICTIONARY TO FIND OUT THE DIFFERENCE BETWEEN STRATEGY AND TACTICS!

LET'S GO, KOKUKIRIN!
ZAT
HEY, WAIT!

WHAT'RE YOU GOING TO DO IF TAIKOBO INVADES WHILE YOU'RE GONE?!

LORD BUNCHU SAID HE'LL LEAVE IT UP TO ME TO HANDLE THE TRAITOR TAIKOBO!

THERE-FORE...

I'D LIKE YOU TO LET *ME* HANDLE THINGS INSTEAD.

CHOKEI... YOU ARE A TALENTED FIGHTER...

BUT YOU MIGHT BE DUPED BY THE SCHEMER TAIKOBO.

GRR

ALL RIGHT THEN.

BUNCHU WENT TO KINGO ISLAND? ♡
YES, DAKKI!

CHOKOMEI. ♡
CREAK

BUT WHY DIDN'T YOU WANT BUNCHU TO KNOW THAT YOU CAME UP WITH THAT IDEA?
BECAUSE, BUNCHU AND I HATE EACH OTHER'S GUTS. ♡

BUT NOW I CAN PLAY WITH TAIKOBO WHILE BUNCHU'S AWAY. ♡
YOU'RE ONE WICKED WOMAN!

Kingo Islands

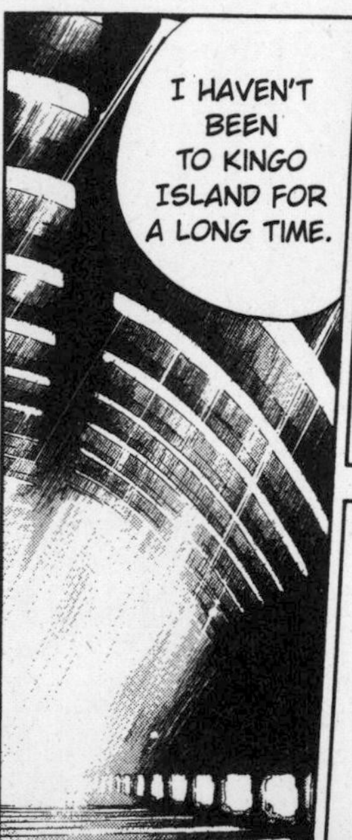

SUT

FLASH
!!

WHAT ?!
GWOON

OH?
BUNCHU, IS THAT YOU?!
YOTENKUN!

AH, I SUPPOSE YOU DIDN'T KNOW ABOUT THIS.
WE'RE PROTECTING LORD TSUTEN KYOSHU WITH THE JUZETSUJIN, THE ALTERNATE DIMENSION THAT WE JUTTENKUN CREATE.
WE JUTTENKUN ARE A LITTLE CONFUSED.
WHOEVER TRIES TO APPROACH LORD TSUTEN KYOSHU WITHOUT PERMISSION IS DRAGGED INTO THE JUZETSUJIN AND EXECUTED.
THE JUZET-SUJIN...
FINE.
BUT YOTENKUN... WHY DIDN'T YOU ANSWER MY SUMMONS?
...
DO YOU REALLY NEED OUR HELP?

JUTTENKUN, HOW COULD YOU?!

Meanwhile, at the fortress Yozen built...

AMAZING, YOZEN!

I'VE NEVER SEEN SUCH A SECURE FORTRESS!

THANK YOU... WE'RE AT THE BORDER OF YIN AND ZHOU...

...SO I BUILT A FORTRESS THAT FULFILLS OUR REQUIREMENTS!

GOOD!

ZAT

YOU KID OVER THERE... ARE YOU TAIKOBO?

HMM?

GASP
UH, SUSU...
WHO IS IT?
GWOO
GA GA GA GA
Y-YES... THAT'S...

READ
THIS
WAY

GLARE

WH-WHAT A SMALL GUY...
NO, IT'S THE CREA- TURE THAT'S HUGE.

TAIKOBO, MY NAME IS TOH KYUKO!
AND I'M THE YOSEI RYUSHUKO.

BLAH BLAH
BY THE ORDERS OF THE LORD OF HEAVEN, KING CHU, I HAVE COME TO BRING A CHARGE AGAINST YOUR MASTER, KING BU!
HE IGNORED THE LORD OF HEAVEN, KING CHU, AND DECLARED HIMSELF KING BU. HE HAS GIVEN PROTECTION TO THE TRAITOR HIKO KO. HE'S INSTIGATED THE PEOPLE TO INVADE CHOKA.

STEAM
EVEN HEAVEN WILL NOT FORGIVE THESE GRAVE SINS! I CANNOT OVERLOOK THIS!
I'LL CUT YOU DOWN WITH MY SWORD, YOU TRAI- TORS!

OH?

BOING

BOING

THAT VOICE...

DADDY?!

!

DADDY?

MISS SPY!
!

DOES THIS MEAN YOU'LL BE OUR ENEMY NOW?

GULP

SORRY, SUPU.
I'LL MISS YOU...

...BUT THIS IS MY FATE!
OH NO!
LEAP
MISS SPY!

WELL, ALL RIGHT. THEY DON'T LOOK TOO STRONG.
AND THE SPY'S PAOPE ISN'T SUITED FOR FIGHTING.

TMP

DADDY, RYUSHUKO... LONG TIME NO SEE!

SENGYOKU, YOU'RE NOT HURT?

SEN, LONG TIME NO SEE!

GRR

DADDY, THOSE GUYS ARE TERRIBLE!

THEY SAY I'M WEAK AND WON'T TAKE ME SERIOUSLY!

RYUSHUKO! GO GET THEM!

SWING

YOU GOT IT!

WHAT?!

Y-Y-YOU IMPUDENT FOOLS!

GAGAGA

封神
演義

GYAOO
Chapter 69
DOKOSON SNEAKS IN AT NIGHT

RYUSHUKO, THANKS FOR COMING! I APPRECIATE YOUR FRIENDSHIP!

YOU'RE MY BEST FRIEND, SEN! ANYBODY WHO BULLIES YOU WILL GET IT!

THAT STUPID TAIKOBO BULLIED ME WEARING A BIRD SUIT!

OOPS

WHAT?! IS THAT TRUE, SEN-GYOKU?

THAT'S TERRIBLE!

YOU'RE GONNA PAY FOR THAT!

BAM

GWOO!!

ZUGAGA

D...DARN. THE FORTRESS WILL BE DESTROYED.

YOZEN! WE'LL TAKE THEM DOWN!

NO!

HUH?

I DON'T MIND FIGHTING THE YOSEI RYUSHUKO AND DADDY, BUT THE SPY'S PAOPE IS HORRIFYING...

THE READERS WOULDN'T WANT TO SEE MY WEIRDLY EROTIC FACE, EITHER!

UH... THE MALE READERS MIGHT WANT TO SEE THAT...

OH NO, THEY WON'T!

WHAT'S GOING ON, TAIKOBO?!

CLATTER CLATTER

AN ENEMY ATTACK?!

AH! GOOD TO HAVE YOU HERE!

LISTEN, HERE'S WHAT'S GOING ON...

READ
THIS
WAY

HMM...
GIMME A BREAK...

WELL ...
...LET'S GO BACK ABOUT A MONTH.
GAAA

Mount Kongrong Kiringai

!
WHISTLE

HYOO

DOKOSON!

DOKOSON APPEARED IN VOLUME 3, INTERLUDE 1. HE'S THE DISCIPLE OF KURYUSON, ONE OF THE 12 ELITE SENNIN WHO LIVES IN HIUNDO, MOUNT KYORYU. HE HAS THE PAOPE DORYUSO THAT ALLOWS HIM TO MOVE UNDERGROUND.

MASTER TOLD ME TO GO TO TAIKOBO'S PLACE.

A LOT OF OUR PEOPLE GOT HURT, SO I'M FILLING IN FOR THEM UNTIL THEY GET BETTER.

GWOO

THERE IT IS!

WHIZ
WHIZ
TIP
HUH?
BAM
BAM
KA WHAM BOOM
!!

READ
THIS
WAY

OH MY GOSH, WHAT IS IT?!
A... A BIRD?! DID WE HIT A BIRD?!

HMM...NO, SENGYOKU.
SHP
IT'S A STRANGE-LOOKING CREATURE.

OUCH.
WHAT THE HECK...

TMP

!
DOKOSON?!
DOKOSON!

WHOA, A TOTALLY HOT CHICK!
GAA
HII
GOTTA ASK HER OUT ON A DRIVE!

AH...
...A REIJU!

OH...
... REALLY ?

HEY! LET'S GO BEYOND THE RAINBOW ON MY FERRARI!
I'M A YOSEI, SO I CAN'T FLY.
THAT IDIOT GOES AFTER *ANY* GIRL!

SO... WHAT'S YOUR NAME?
STEP
I'M DOKOSON!
DOKOSON!
YOU'RE SUPER-CUTE!
CLENCH

SLAM

GRAB
HEH HEH HEH HEH HEH...

WHA?

DADDY! I LIKE THIS GUY, SO I'M GOING OUT WITH HIM!
SE... SENGYOKU ?!

READ THIS WAY

'CUZ HE SAID I'M A HOT CHICK!
THAT'S LIKE ASKING ME TO MARRY HIM!

STRUGGLE
L-LEMME GO!
WRIGGLE
BUT DEAR... YOU DON'T HAVE TO GO OUT WITH A MONSTER LIKE THIS.

WHAT ABOUT THAT GUY OVER THERE INSTEAD?
I THINK HE'S GOT POTENTIAL ...

NO! HE'S HANDSOME, BUT HE'S NOT MY TYPE!
...
YOU'VE GOT STRANGE TASTE IN MEN.
BLAST IT!
SHE'S HOT, BUT SHE'S A WEIRDO!

ALL RIGHT, ALL RIGHT! LET ME DOWN!

SURE!

THERE!

PA

DASH

OH NO!

DIVE

DIG DIG DIG

CRACKLE
CRACKLE
That night

...
I'M SO APPALLED, I HAVE NOTHING TO SAY.
PLEASE, PORSCHE. I SURRENDER THIS TIME.

BUT A GIRL FINALLY FELL FOR YOU. WHY'D YOU RUN AWAY? THIS IS PROBABLY YOUR LAST CHANCE!

SH-SHUT UP. I'M PARTICULAR ABOUT MY WOMAN!

HMM... YOU KNOW...

...WE MIGHT BE ABLE TO TAKE ADVANTAGE OF THIS.

WHAT?!
YOU WANT ME TO CONVINCE HER TO BECOME OUR ALLY?!

WE'RE HAVING PROBLEMS DEALING WITH THAT SPY. THE EASIEST THING IS TO HAVE HER SWITCH SIDES.
HUFF
N-NO WAY! NEVER!
HMM ...

ALL RIGHT..; YOZEN!
VWM
YES!

...
MAYBE I WAS TOO MEAN TO THAT GIRL...

MR. MOLE!
STEP

H...
... HEKIUN!

SPARKLING
I HEARD YOU'RE GOING TO GO PERSUADE THE ENEMY! YOU'RE SO BRAVE! YOU'RE WONDERFUL!
AND IF YOU SUCCEED, TAIKOBO WILL LET YOU USE SUPUSHAN FOR FREE AS A REWARD!

DADDY, I...
SSS
...SEEM TO HAVE A WEAKNESS...

...FOR THIS SORT OF SILHOUETTE.
I SEE.

GO TO BED NOW! STAYING UP LATE IS BAD FOR YOUR SKIN.
RYUSHUKO AND I WILL KEEP WATCH!
YEEES!

ZZZ
ZZZ

POP
ZZZ
ZZZ

PERSUADE HER?
HOW THE HECK DO I DO THAT?

ZZZ
ZZZ
UH...
SHE'S ALL RIGHT IF SHE DOESN'T TALK.
BA-BUMP
BA-BUMP
BLINK

HOSHIN ENGI, VOL. 8 - THE END

***Hoshin Engi* Secret Characters Encyclopedia! Part 6**

At-A-Glance *Hoshin* Relationship Chart

Part 1

Seiki = Zhou

The Great War between Zhou and Yin is about to begin. Today we review the people of Zhou and their relationships, focusing on Taikobo.

November is *Hoshin* Month! Four-weeks-in-a-row special.

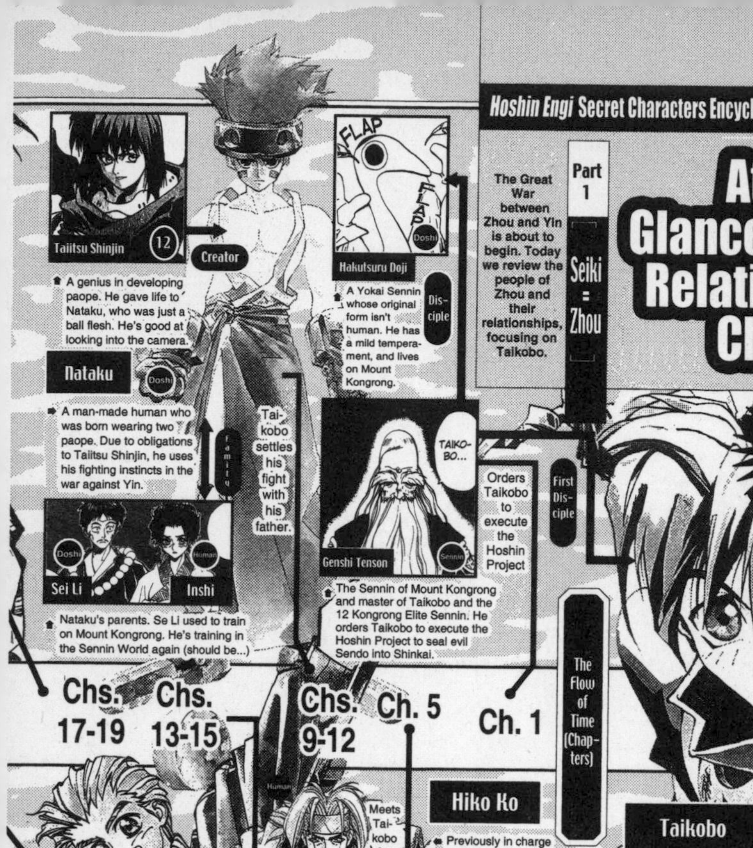

Taiitsu Shinjin (12)

A genius in developing paope. He gave life to Nataku, who was just a ball flesh. He's good at looking into the camera.

Hakutsuru Doji (Doshi)

A Yokai Sennin whose original form isn't human. He has a mild temperament, and lives on Mount Kongrong.

Nataku (Doshi)

A man-made human who was born wearing two paope. Due to obligations to Taiitsu Shinjin, he uses his fighting instincts in the war against Yin.

Sei Li (Doshi) **Inshi** (Human)

Nataku's parents. Se Li used to train on Mount Kongrong. He's training in the Sennin World again (should be...)

Genshi Tenson (Sennin)

The Sennin of Mount Kongrong and master of Taikobo and the 12 Kongrong Elite Sennin. He orders Taikobo to execute the Hoshin Project to seal evil Sendo into Shinkai.

The Flow of Time (Chapters)

Chs. 17-19 — Chs. 13-15 — Chs. 9-12 — Ch. 5 — Ch. 1

Hiko Ko (Human)

Meets Taikobo for the first time.

Previously in charge of Yin's military affairs. Even after Dakki the Sennyo bewitched the Emperor King Chu, he was served Yin.

Taikobo (Doshi)

The hero of this story. To execute the Hoshin Project, he challenges Dakki of Yi (Choka), who is neglecting the people. He fights alone at first, but realizes the limits of his power and begins to gather comrades to fight with him. Now, he's the leader of Zhou, which has risen up against Yin. He's good at using his brains in battle.

Asks Taikobo to take him in as a disciple.

Bukichi (Human)

He used to be a lumberjack. Now he's Taikobo's assistant. He's never trained in the Sennin World, but he can run faster than anyone.

Vehicle

Supushan

Genshi Tenson gave this reiju to Taikobo. He can fly and is proud of his speed! He has a very serious character.

Tests Taikobo and becomes his comrade.

Yozen (Doshi)

A genius Doshi, the only one who can perform miracles with his jutsu without using paope! Genshi Tenson orders him to cooperate with the Hoshin Project.

Disciple

By Kisosha

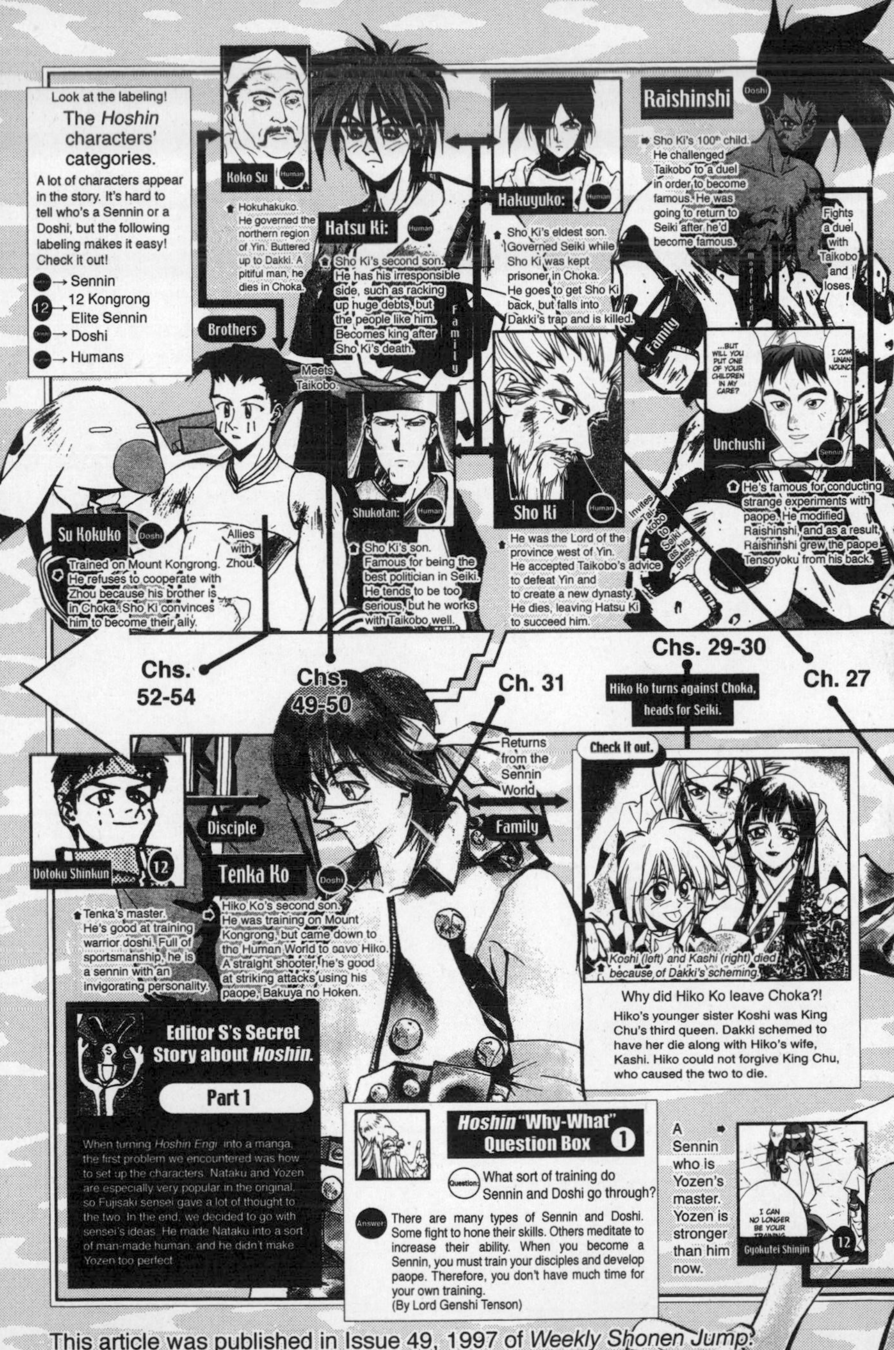

This article was published in Issue 49, 1997 of *Weekly Shonen Jump*.

Hoshin Engi Secret Characters Encyclopedia!!
Part 7
At-a-Glance Hoshin Relationship Chart
Part 2
Yin = Choka chapter
Last time, we explained about Zhou. This time, we review the relationships on the Yin side! Here is data gathered by Taikobo and his comrades about their fighting abilities and danger ratings!
November is Hoshin Month! Four-weeks-in-a-row special.
Every-thing is going just as I wanted. ♡
Uses the Temptation Jutsu to manipulate him.
Dakki and her sisters
Kibi
Doshi
The second sister. She looks rather dim, but she can use more than two paope at once.
Don't be fooled by her cuteness!
Danger rating ★★★
Okijin
Doshi
The youngest sister. She's straightforward, but her paope attacks using powders of poisonous moths are difficult to deal with!
She fell into my trap the first time, but she won't fall for it the next time around.
Danger rating ★★★
Dakki and I are one in body and spirit!
The 30th emperor of the Yin Dynasty. He has a weakness for women, but he is a master in the arts of the pen and the sword. Dakki turned him into a foolish ruler, and she seems to be modifying his body as well.
Even if he's king, he's an ordinary human, right? What, he's won against the Buseio?!
King Chu
Human
Danger rating ★★
Neutral
Neutral
Just to let you know, I'm not on anybody's side.
Kokutenko
A reiju that Shinkohyo rides. He is famous for being the strongest reiju, but it's not clear what his abilities are.
He has a ferocious gaze! I was scared when he glared at me.
Danger rating ★★★★
Vehicle
Shinkohyo
Doshi
Danger rating ★★★★★
Listed first on the Hoshin List. He's the strongest Doshi and is said to be stronger than the Three Great Sennin. He has the strongest paope, the Raikoben. He is Dakki's guest, but it doesn't look as if he'll participate in the battle between Zhou and Yin.
What is he thinking? I can't understand him. He really is strong, though.
Yin is full of strong characters. But they don't seem to trust each other completely. We may be able to take advantage of that.
Those who retired from battle.
Mareiju
Attacked Zhou with the giant paope Kakoten. But Yozen destroys all of the Kakoten.
Furin, Chokeiho
Bunchu sent them to stop Hiko and his clan from reaching Seiki. Keiho's paope Kyumeikon freezes the enemy, and Furin's paope Koju captures them. They caught Taikobo and his party, but in the end, they were sealed by Tenka and Nataku.
Kohei, Ryono, Koso
Dakki sent these assassins when Hiko turned against Yin and headed for Seiki. The three were all Yokai Sennin, but Hiko sealed Kohei, and Tenka sealed the other two. They weren't too strong. They were used to make Bunchu serious about killing Hiko.
Hohitsu, Hoso
They came after Inchon and Inchi, King Chu's princes, when the two fled from Dakki. The two are Yokai Sennin whose original form are minerals. They fought Taikobo, but in the end, they were free from Dakki's Temptation Jutsu and disappeared somewhere.
Chinto
A Yokai Sennin who fought Taikobo when he was about to attack a village of a foreign tribe under Dakki's orders. He used the paope Karyuhyo to fight but fell into Taikobo's trap and was sealed.

Look at the labeling!

The *Hoshin* characters are categorized into:

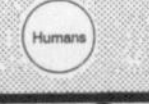

CHECK this out.

Why won't Bunchu leave Yin?!

Bunchu had a rival named Shushi. They both became generals of Yin, but Shushi became a queen and dies in battle, leaving her child behind. Shushi's child became the next king. Since then, Bunchu decided to serve Yin by becoming a tutor to the Royal Family of Yin.

King Chu is one of the kings that Bunchu tutored. Even if his best friend Hiko abandons the king, Bunchu cannot forsake Yin, who has raised generations of kings!

Chokomei (Doshi)

An envoy sent from Kingo Island, he relays Tsuten Kyoshu's message to Bunchu. He also forces Dakki and Bunchu to make peace with each other. He's frivolous but seems to be as strong as both Dakki and Bunchu.

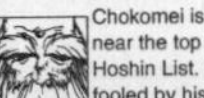

Chokomei is listed near the top of the Hoshin List. Don't be fooled by his looks!

Yes indeed! We'll have a ball tonight.

Danger rating ★★★★

Juttenkun (Sennin)

Sennin of Kingo Island. They're the equivalent of the 12 Kongrong Elite Sennin. They're backing Bunchu up under Tsuten Kyoshu's orders!

Danger rating ★★★★★

Tsuten Kyoshu (Sennin)

One of the Great Sennin. Bunchu's master. The head of Kingo Islands! Backs up Bunchu fully to defeat Kongrong.

Danger rating ★★★★★

Master

Cooperate

Dakki (Sennin)

She's the head of over 300 Sennin and Doshi. She spent many hundreds of years perfecting the Temptation Jutsu. She uses the jutsu to manipulate King Chu and obtain the highest status. She is extremely beautiful but also cruel. She is more cunning than Taikobo and can fight well, too!

A very dangerous Sennyo. She caused Yin to fall into chaos. It is fun transforming into her, though.

Danger rating ★★★★★

Enemies

Bunchu: (Doshi)

Taishi (Gunshi) of Yin. Doshi of Kingo Island. He has served the Yin Dynasty for many years. He opposes Zhou, which has risen up against Yin. However, he's also an enemy of Dakki, who manipulates King Chu and has caused chaos in Yin. He has amazing fighting abilities, using his paope Kinden to strike his enemies!

Danger rating ★★★★★

I'd like to have him as our ally...he's a formidable enemy.

It is not too late! Yin will always rise again!

Subject

Bunchu and his subjects

Sends her to spy on Zhou.

Subject

The Shisei of Kuryu Islands

Fights for Bunchu

Four Doshi who live in Kuryu Island, One of the Kingo Islands. They have previously fought alongside Bunchu and have battled with Taikobo and his comrades to stop Hiko Ko from heading to Seiki. They are professional warriors, and have amazing fighting abilities. The Shisei and Bunchu together have fought and defeated Dakki and her sisters in the past.

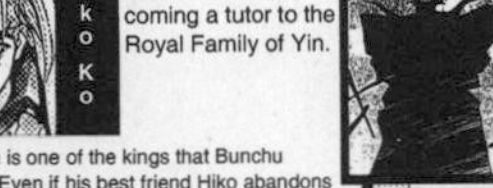

All of them have amazing destructive power. They're bothersome to deal with. The next time we fight, we'll end it quickly so they don't cause so much damage.

Danger rating ★★★★★

Chokei (Doshi)

Bunchu's subordinate. He worries about the busy Bunchu's health. He's a Doshi but is now in the Forbidden Castle. He hasn't participated in battles directly.

Never seen this guy. Who is he?

Danger rating ★

Toh Sengyoku (Doshi)

She calls herself the beautiful spy. Sent by Bunchu. She talks a lot, wants to stand out from the crowd... we can't figure out why Bunchu sent her in as a spy. She won the match against Taikobo and is happily recognized as an official spy by Zhou.

She is our enemy, but she's actually cute. Pudding ♡

Danger rating ★★

Editor S's Secret Story about *Hoshin*

Part2

About the trip to China...as mentioned in Issue 44, Fujisaki sensei (finally) was able to go to China in the summer of '97. Readers tend to overlook it, but the backgrounds and buildings in the manga are largely based on historical sites that actually exist. During this trip, sensei bought new reference materials and took lots of photos. He didn't even take one souvenir photograph.

Hoshin "Why-What" Question Box ②

Question: Is it true that there are two types of Sennin (Doshi), those who are human and those who are not?

Answer: Yes, there are! Even if you're not human, if they're exposed to moonlight and sunlight for a thousand years, animals and objects can turn Sennin! Kibi's original form isn't human, but she became a Doshi! Be nice to animals and things!
(By Kibi)

Maka Yonsho

Mareisei	Mareiko	Mareikai
He defeated Tenka once with the paope sword Seiunken, which cuts the enemies many times with one swing.	His paope Kongensan repels enemy attacks. Nataku almost destroys the Kongensan, and this is their undoing.	He attacks with the nerve disrupting paope Kurobiwa. In the end he's defeated by Yozen along with the other three.

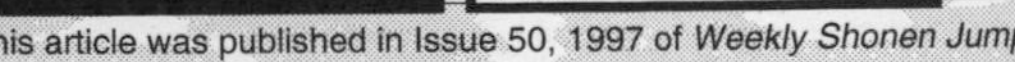

This article was published in Issue 50, 1997 of *Weekly Shonen Jump*.

MISS (trans. verb)

1) To fail to hit, reach or contact <~ the target>
2) ~ A deadline. To fail to deliver a manuscript on time, so it is not published.
3) The most dishonorable thing that could happen to a mangaka. Those who miss a deadline are called "scum mangaka."

Emergency Press Conference!

How did Ryu Fujisaki miss his deadline for "The Sheer Precipice, Where Is It Now? 11"?!

In place of "The Sheer Precipice, Where Is It Now? 11."

MR. FUJISAKI, WHY DID YOU MISS THE DEADLINE THIS TIME?

Reporters

I WAS ASLEEP.

THAT'S THE REASON?! YOU'RE A MANGAKA!

WHY DON'T YOU JUST DIE?!

ARE YOU STUPID?!

OH, I'M SORRY. I'M SORRY.

GAAA

BUT FUJISAKI, IF YOU HAVE THE ENERGY TO DRAW THIS, DRAW THE "SHEER PRECIPICE"...

GAH!

SPLAT

I APOLOGIZE TO THE READERS WHO WERE EXPECTING A PROPER "THE SHEER PRECIPICE, WHERE IS IT NOW?"

OH NO!

FLASH

I WON'T READ YOUR MANGA ANYMORE!

STOP DRAWING MANGA!

I'LL DRAW #12 WITHOUT MISSING MY DEADLINE, SO PLEASE FORGIVE ME.

Hoshin Engi: The Rank File!

You'll find as you read *Hoshin Engi* that there are titles and ranks that you are probably unfamiliar with. While it may seem confusing, there is an order to the madness that is pulled from ancient Chinese mythology, Japanese culture, other manga, and, of course, the incredible mind of *Hoshin Engi* creator Ryu Fujisaki.

Where we think it will help, we give you a hint in the margin on the page the name appears. But in addition, here's a quick primer on the titles you'll find in *Hoshin Engi* and what they mean:

Japanese	Title	Job Description
武成王	Buseio	Chief commanding officer
宰相	Saisho	Premier
太師	Taishi	The king's advisor/tutor
大金剛	Dai Kongo	Great Vassals
軍師	Gunshi	Military tactician
大諸侯	Daishoko	Great feudal lord
東伯侯	Tohakuko	Lord of the east region
西伯侯	Seihakuko	Lord of the west region
北伯侯	Hokuhakuko	Lord of the north region
南伯侯	Nanhakuko	Lord of the south region

Hoshin Engi: The Immortal File

Also, you'll probably find the hierarchy of the Sennin, Sendo and Doshi somewhat complicated. Here, we spell it out the easiest way possible!

Japanese	Title	Description
道士	Doshi	Someone training to become Sennin
仙道	Sendo	Used to describe both Sennin and Doshi
仙人	Sennin	Those who have mastered the way. Once you "go Sennin" you are forever changed.
妖孽	Yogetsu	A Yosei who can transform into a human
妖怪仙人	Yokai Sennin	A Sennin whose original form is not human
妖精	Yosei	An animal or object exposed to moonlight and sunlight for more than 1,000 years

Hoshin Engi: The Magical File

Paope (宝貝) are powerful magical items used by Sennin and Doshi. Sometimes they look like regular objects, like a veil or hat. These are just a few of the magical items, both paope and otherwise, that you'll encounter in *Hoshin Engi!*

Japanese	Magic	Description
打神鞭	Dashinben	Known as the God-Striking Whip, Taikobo's pao manipulates the air and wind.
霊獣	Reiju	A magical flying beast that Sennin and Doshi us for transportation and support. Taikobo's reiju is his pal Supu.
雷公鞭	Raikoben	Reduces an opponent to ashes with a huge clap of thunder.
哮天犬	Kotenken	The Howling Dog can fly and be used as an attack paope.
莫邪の宝剣	Bakuya no Hoken	Tenka's weapon, a light saber.
禁鞭	Kinben	A powerful whip that can attack anything in a diameter of several kilometers.
花狐貂	Kakoten	An object that consumes people and cities for its energy source.
青雲剣	Seiunken	A sword with a blade that splits into many blades when swung.
混元傘	Kongensan	Absorbs the enemy attacks and uses them a attackers.
黒琵琶	Kurobiwa	A lute that manipulates the minds of those who hear it.
拌黄珠	Bankoju	A vehicle that shoots energy beams.
開天珠	Kaitenju	A missile that destroys anything it touches. Allows the user to fly.
紫綬羽衣	Shiju Hagoromo	Allows the user to fly, and emits a lethal poison moth powder.
傾世元禳	Keisei Genjo	An object that radiates the perfume of temptation.
鑽心釘	Sanshintei	Dagger-like version of Bakuya no Hoken.
五光石	Gokoseki	A rock that changes the face of whomever it strikes into a "weirdly macho-looking" face.
十絶陣	Juzetsujin	An alternate dimension that can envelop and conceal places in the real world.

Coming Next Volume: The Princes' Choice

The two princes return from their training on Mount Kongrong and must now take sides in the great war between Yin and Seiki. Will they use their newly developed powers to support their father or to oppose their mother's murderer?

AVAILABLE OCTOBER 2008!

Read Any Good Books Lately?

Hoshin Engi is based on *Fengshen Yanji (The Creation of the Gods,* written in the 1500s by Xu Zhonglin) one of China's four classic fantastical novels of adventure, magic and mystery. The other three are *Saiyuki (Journey to the West* by Cheng'en Wu, late 1500s), *Sangokushi Engi (Romance of the Three Kingdoms* by Guanzhong Luo), and *Shui Hu Zhuan* (*Outlaws of the Marsh,* by Shi Nai'an, mid-1500s).

Want to read these books? You can! They're all still in print, more than 500 years later!

These books are North American in-print editions only.

MANGA
ON SALE NOW!

LUFFY HAS VOWED TO BECOME KING OF THE PIRATES AND FIND THE LEGENDARY TREASURE KNOWN AS "ONE PIECE"!

SHONEN JUMP MANGA

On sale at:
www.shonenjump.com
Also available at your local bookstore and comic store.

www.viz.com

Tell us what you think about SHONEN JUMP manga!

Our survey is now available online.
Go to: ***www.SHONENJUMP.com/mangasurvey***

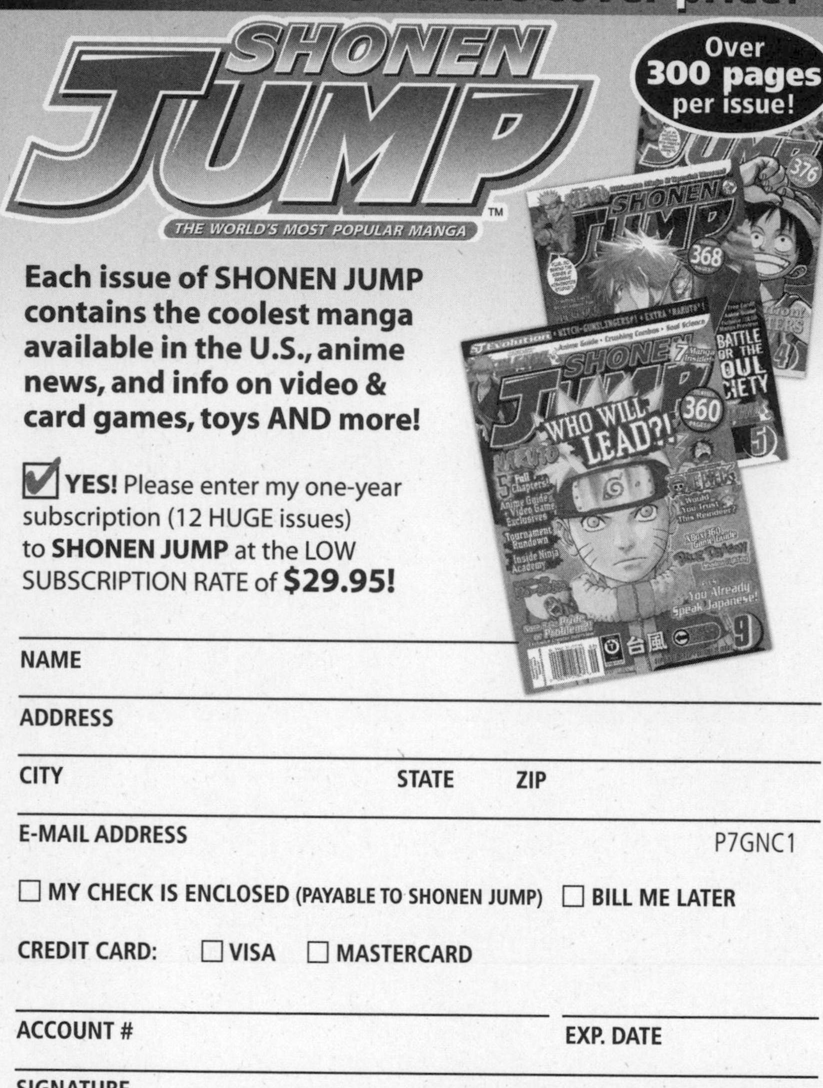
Save 50% OFF the cover price!
SHONEN JUMP
THE WORLD'S MOST POPULAR MANGA
Over 300 pages per issue!
Each issue of SHONEN JUMP contains the coolest manga available in the U.S., anime news, and info on video & card games, toys AND more!
YES! Please enter my one-year subscription (12 HUGE issues) to SHONEN JUMP at the LOW SUBSCRIPTION RATE of $29.95!
NAME
ADDRESS
CITY
STATE
ZIP
E-MAIL ADDRESS
P7GNC1
MY CHECK IS ENCLOSED (PAYABLE TO SHONEN JUMP)
BILL ME LATER
CREDIT CARD:
VISA
MASTERCARD
ACCOUNT #
EXP. DATE
SIGNATURE
CLIP AND MAIL TO
SHONEN JUMP
Subscriptions Service Dept.
P.O. Box 515
Mount Morris, IL 61054-0515

NARUTO
BONUS! Attach this sticker to the back of the entry form that's also in this product.
40th WEEKLY JUMP
Story and Art by Masashi Kishimoto
NARUTO © 1999 by Masashi Kishimoto/SHUEISHA Inc.
For promotional use only. Not for sale. Printed in USA.
RATED T FOR TEEN
ratings.viz.com
This sticker goes on the 40th anniversary poster from SHONEN JUMP magazine!
Find out how to get the collectible poster (while supplies last) by visiting www.shonenjump.com/wsj40.